KT-116-507

# Daytime
### and
# Night-time
### Animals

## Mark Carwardine

## Illustrated by Martin Camm

Cover illustrations: a screech owl and a chimpanzee

ISBN 1-899-762-20-5

Copyright © 1988 Ilex Publishers Limited
This edition © 1997 Horus Editions Limited

This edition first published 1997 by
Horus Editions Limited, 1st Floor,
27 Longford Street, London NW1 3DZ

All rights reserved. No part of this publication
may be reproduced, stored in a retrieval system, or
transmitted in any form or by any means, electronic,
mechanical, photocopying, recording, or otherwise,
without the permission of the publisher.

Printed in Singapore

# Contents

# The Lemur

## The lemur is a daytime animal.

It spends most of the day looking for food such as fruit, leaves, and insects.

Ring-tailed lemurs can leap easily from tree to tree. But they do not feel as safe as other lemurs or monkeys that move around in the trees. They prefer to have their feet firmly on the ground.

This baby ring-tailed lemur is riding on its mother's back. It has a long, black-and-white tail, just like hers. When these lemurs walk or run along the ground, they always hold their tails in the air, in the shape of a question mark. They use their tails to show their friends where they are.

# The Genet

## The genet is a night-time animal.

It spends most of the day fast asleep, curled up in a hollow tree, under a bush, or in tall grass. But it comes out after dark and spends most of the night hunting. Silently, it searches the forest for insects, birds, lizards, snakes, mice, and other small animals. This genet has

spotted
something
running around
on the forest floor.
   Genets look rather like
cats, but they are much thinner
and have shorter legs.

# The Pelican

## The pelican is a daytime animal.

It spends the day fishing in lakes with lots of other pelicans. All the birds sit on the water, dip their heads under the surface, and scoop up their prey.

This pelican has just swallowed an enormous fish. A pouch under its beak is used as a net for fishing underwater.

Many people are wrong in thinking that the pouch is used for storing fish.

# The Owl

## The owl is a night-time animal.

It can see very well in the dark and can hear the faintest sounds. This screech owl is on the look-out for its supper. It can catch moths and other insects in mid-air, with a loud snap of its bill. It can also catch animals on the ground or on a branch, with its feet.

Screech owls are
very difficult to see
during the daytime.
If they stay
perfectly still,
they look just
like branches.
Sometimes they
lift up their ear
tufts, and squeeze up their
faces, to try and hide.

# The Chimpanzee

## The chimpanzee is a daytime animal.

It lives in the jungles and grasslands of Africa. It is a very clever animal. Chimpanzees are similar to people in many ways. Sometimes they hold hands when they are together or kiss when they meet. Unlike most other monkeys and apes, they also use

home-made tools to find and catch
some of their food. This baby
chimpanzee is watching its mother use
a twig to collect ants from a nest.

# The Badger

## The badger is a night-time animal.

It spends the day underground in a jungle of tunnels and rooms, called a sett. But it comes out of the sett, carefully and quietly, at dusk or during the night. At first it sniffs the air for any signs of danger. Then it stands outside one of the holes to have a

good scratch, before trotting off into the darkness to search for food.

This badger is having a spring-clean, replacing the old bedding from its sett with new leaves and grasses.

# The Marine Iguana

## The marine iguana is a daytime animal.

It spends every day sunbathing on rocks beside the sea. Thousands of marine iguanas lie out on the rocks along the beautiful shores of the Galapagos Islands. These islands are far away off the coast of South America.

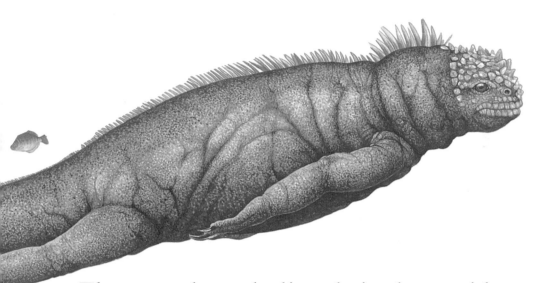

They are the only lizards in the world
that like to live in and around the sea.
  This marine iguana is having a swim,
moving through the water like a snake.
It is looking for seaweed and other
underwater plants to eat.

# The Fox

## The fox is a night-time animal.

It can often be seen running across the road in the middle of the night.

Foxes are common animals in towns and cities, as well as in the countryside. Some foxes have even made their underground dens, called earths, in the middle of people's flower beds.

This fox is pouncing. It is leaping high into the air before diving onto an unlucky mouse – which has no idea the fox is there.

# The Kangaroo

## The kangaroo is a daytime animal.

It leaps and bounds across the grass-lands of Australia and New Guinea. Kangaroos can run very fast, using their long legs to jump and their tails to keep their balance in mid-air. But they move slowly when they are feeding, often using their giant tails as stools to sit on.

This kangaroo has a
tiny baby, called a joey, in
her pouch. The joey stays in the
safety of the pouch for
several months, before setting out
to explore the world.

# The Bat

## The bat is a night-time animal.

It is able to fly around at night without bumping into things. It does not use its eyes, and cannot see in the dark. Instead, it listens very carefully for echoes and other sounds nearby. In this way, it builds up a 'sound picture' of its surroundings.

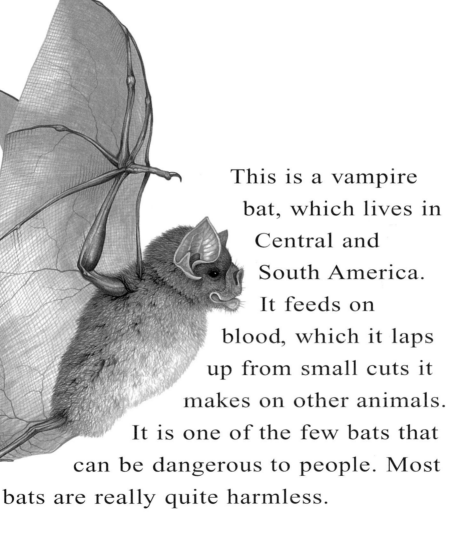

This is a vampire
bat, which lives in
Central and
South America.
It feeds on
blood, which it laps
up from small cuts it
makes on other animals.
It is one of the few bats that
can be dangerous to people. Most
bats are really quite harmless.

# Glossary

**ear tufts** the long head-feathers found on some owls. They have nothing to do with hearing.
**earth** a fox's underground home
**echo** any sound which has bounced off a wall, tree, rock, or some other surface
**joey** a young kangaroo
**mongoose** a small, meat-eating animal
**prey** any animal that is hunted, killed, and then eaten by another animal
**sett** a badger's underground home

# Index